Life story books
for people with learning disabilities
a practical guide

Helen Hewitt

British Library Cataloguing in Publication Data

A CIP record for this book is available
from the Public Library

© BILD Publications 2006

BILD Publications is the imprint of:

British Institute of Learning Disabilities
Campion House
Green Street
Kidderminster
Worcestershire DY10 1JL

Telephone: 01562 723010
Fax: 01562 723029
E-mail: enquiries@bild.org.uk
Website: www.bild.org.uk

ISBN 1 904082 76 9

BILD Publications are distributed by:

BookSource
32 Finlas Street
Cowlairs Estate
Glasgow G22 5DU

Telephone: 08702 402 182
Fax: 0141 557 0189

Printed in the UK by Latimer Trend &
Company Ltd, Plymouth

For a publications catalogue with details
of all BILD books and journals telephone
01562 723010, e-mail enquiries@bild.org.uk
or visit the BILD website www.bild.org.uk

Contents

Introduction
Using this book

This is a practical guide to life story books for people with learning disabilities. The chapters are in a particular order so that you consider certain issues before embarking on a life story project. For this reason it is recommended that you initially read it in a serial fashion. However, once you are familiar with these issues each time you approach a new project you can use the chapters as appropriate. They do work in isolation and may help to remind you of certain elements such as interview techniques or variations for presenting life story information.

All case studies and examples used in this book are based on real people but names and other details have been changed in order to maintain anonymity. Where this is not the case it is stated at the relevant juncture.

The book has eight chapters which are summarised below.

Chapter 1 introduces the concept of life story books, what they are and the benefits of using them. It explains how life story books are linked to identity and why an understanding of identity is essential to our ability both to understand who the person is and to capture it in their life story book.

Chapter 2 provides an overview of how life story books can be used with different client groups. These include: more able people who require little help to compile their book and can express how they wish to use them; older people who can use them as an aid to reminiscence; people with challenging behaviour who can use the books to come to terms with traumatic events they have experienced; and people with profound learning disabilities who can use the books to highlight and maintain their identity, especially across transitions in care.

Chapter 3 is particularly important as it highlights the ethical considerations you need to take into account before embarking on a life story project. These include issues of consent, ownership and dealing with traumatic events. Advice is given to ensure the life story books and all the people involved with them are treated with respect and handled sensitively.

Chapter 4 focuses on the issue of inclusion. It examines ways in which you can encourage participation from the people whose books you are helping to produce. Even people with very profound learning disabilities can be involved at some level in the compilation of their life story books.

Chapter 5 aims to motivate you to begin preparing a life story book. It emphasises how easily this can be done. Advice is given for making a start on a project, including easy-to-use checklists.

Chapter 6 sets out in detail the steps needed to gather information for a life story project. These include making contacts, having an interview schedule and sourcing information.

Chapter 7 helps you to make sense of all the information you have gathered. Advice is given on how to write the stories, gain feedback and present the overall book. This chapter also explores the many ways you can present life story information. A simple collage-style poster on a person's wall can constitute a life story book, or a multimedia computerised version can be created. The style will depend on the individual's needs and preferences. Examples and advice are included for recreating the different styles.

Chapter 8 emphasises the fact that a life story book is never complete. It is just a beginning and can be added to at any point. This chapter also summarises the other chapters and highlights the joy and pleasure a life story book can bring, not only to the subject of the book, but for relatives and carers alike. Example quotations are used to emphasise the value of creating life story books for people with learning disabilities. Setting out a person's history encourages others to view them as unique individuals.

Chapter 1
Why life story books?

A life story book is a biographical (or autobiographical) account of a person's life, including stories and memories of past events and relationships – all the kinds of experiences that make us who we are. Life story books have been used in a number of settings as a means of addressing issues regarding a person's identity. People with learning disabilities are often denied the opportunity to consider who they are and how life events affect their identity. This is even more pertinent in the light of current community care where people are faced with many transitions in their lives which can lead to a lack of continuity, and even a loss of identity, if a person's past experiences are not acknowledged.

Even people with very limited abilities can benefit from having a life story book. In addition to helping the person with learning disabilities, these books also enable others to see beyond the 'client' identity and appreciate that each person has a unique life history that sets them apart from other people.

This guide provides easy-to-follow advice for creating life story books for people with learning disabilities. It is aimed at all client groups and levels of ability. It can be used by people with learning disabilities themselves, or by people working with them. The benefits of using life story books makes this guide a valuable resource for all people who are involved in the lives of people with learning disabilities.

Identity and people with learning disabilities

Identity is a broad concept but we all have a notion of what it means. Our identity is what makes us unique. If you were asked the question 'Who are you?' it is likely that you would draw on some or all of the following to define yourself:

- name

- age

- where you live

- educational background

- occupation

- marital status

- whether you have children

- family background

- family relationships

- self-image

- friendships (past and present)

- past experiences

- religious beliefs

- core values (eg vegetarianism)

- likes and dislikes

- hobbies

- dreams and aspirations

If you were to ask a person with learning disabilities the same question they might find it much harder to answer. This is because they are less likely to have an understanding of what identity means, having fewer opportunities than other people to explore some of the items on the list above. They may also find it difficult to hold on to all those elements in a coherent manner.

Issues concerning the identities of people with learning disabilities were traditionally examined within the field of psychology. In the 1950s and 1960s there was a heavy emphasis on personality inventories and rating scales where people were assigned a personality type or set of traits. This was clearly a very limited approach as it assumed that personalities were fixed, with no room for growth and development. Also, the approach relied heavily on rating scales and questionnaires requiring a significant amount of cognitive understanding and verbal competence to complete. This meant that people with more severe and profound learning disabilities were overlooked.

During the 1960s there were two publications which provided a detailed examination of what it was like to have a learning disability at that time. The first was *Cloak of Competence* by Robert Edgerton (1967) and the other was *Stigma* by Irving Goffman (1963). Although over 30 years old, these books are still very relevant and readable today. Both researchers used the ethnographic approach to seeing what life was like in long-stay hospitals. This involved studying a 'people' (in this case people with learning disabilities) in their natural environment to provide a portrait of their lives. The biggest message from both books was that people with learning disabilities were segregated and stigmatised by the rest of society. Goffman talks of a 'spoilt' identity to describe how people were denied an individual identity beyond the learning disability label placed on them by non-disabled others. This is still partly true today, which is why it is essential we understand more about identities and important that we encourage a sense of identity in people with learning disabilities.

In the 1980s there was a major shift in the philosophy of care within learning disabilities, brought on mainly by the concept of 'normalisation' which was first introduced in America by Wolfensberger (1972) and then in Britain by O'Brien and Tyne (1981). Normalisation is the idea that non-valued people will become valued if they are treated like the rest of society. Community integration, which is at the core of this philosophy, drove the deinstitutionalisation movement from the 1980s to the present day. In terms of identity, normalisation was challenged as being repressive to people with learning disabilities as they were encouraged to 'pass as normal' rather than accept their own identity.

More recently there have been attempts to redress this imbalance. Szivos and Griffiths (1990) talk of consciousness raising, which is where people with learning disabilities meet together to share their experiences. The emphasis is on the positive aspects of owning a learning disability identity and helping people to locate the 'handicap' in society rather than themselves. Bogdan and Taylor (1989) looked at the notion of acceptance, rather than stigma, which acknowledges that people with learning disabilities are not stigmatised by all of society. In fact, even within care settings people with learning disabilities can and do engage in some very meaningful relationships with non-disabled others.

Even more recently there has been a shift in how the identities of people with learning disabilities are considered. One new approach is the use of biography and autobiography to learn what it is like to have a learning disability from the people themselves (Atkinson, 1997). There has been a proliferation of published self-testimonies and life stories (Atkinson et al, 2000; Bogdan and Taylor, 1994; Fray, 2000). These not only serve to enlighten but to place people with learning disabilities within our broader cultural history as, traditionally, there has been a huge gap here (Brigham et al, 2000).

Current philosophy of care is based on the recent white paper *Valuing People* (Department of Health, 2001), the main emphasis of which is on social inclusion for people with learning disabilities. In terms of identities, recommendations are set out for care settings to provide person-centred plans for every individual. These aim to place the person at the centre of their care and consider all aspects of their lives. One example is the 'Hello, this is me' model of planning care for children in respite settings which highlights the uniqueness of the child (Laverty and Reet, 2001). Life history information clearly has a place here.

Identity in the care setting

When considering the list of attributes that characterise our identity we can examine how they are taken into account within the care setting. Firstly, it is necessary to look at what forms of documentation about the person in the care setting exist. These are likely to include:

- current care plans
- previous care plans and nursing notes
- medical records
- risk assessments
- pharmacology cards, detailing medication requirements

Exercise 1 – assessing a person-centred care plan

The most commonly used form of documentation in the care setting is likely to be the care plan or person-centred plan (if currently in use). For each of the identity attributes listed above, consider how the care plan in your setting takes account of it if, indeed, it does.

Your answers will vary according to the setting and individuals within the setting. You are likely to find that most elements are documented, although some may not be. The elements that are commonly absent or deficient in care plans include detailed information regarding relationships over the life span of the person and details of their past experiences. These are significant aspects of a person's identity.

Care plans and identity

Care plans are essential documents about the person and it is not the intention of this book to dismiss them. However, in terms of addressing issues relating to a person's identity there are clearly some deficiencies. There are two very good reasons for this. Firstly, it is because a care plan is, by definition, a very function-orientated document. It sets out the care needed for each individual and how to provide it (usually from a nursing perspective). Secondly, identity information such as past experiences is often absent in a care plan because it is future-orientated. Care plans are always kept in the present, with old action plans being filtered out and filed away elsewhere. In other words, care plans are prospective rather than retrospective, which means it is difficult (and inappropriate) to keep the past alive. It would be impossible to keep all previous events in a care plan as it would be too large and not very user friendly.

In order to redress this imbalance some settings have changed to a more person-centred approach to care planning. These are more likely to cover more of the items on the forms of documentation list above. However, another way to highlight the person's identity, by documenting their life history, is to produce a life story book. These books can and should be completely independent of the care plans, although they can definitely complement them.

What is a life story book?

A life story book is a collection of stories and memories that characterise the significant relationships and events over a person's lifetime. There is no one right way to produce life story books as they are unique to each individual.

To illustrate the difference in the kinds of information presented in a life story book and in a care plan a comparison is shown on the following pages. It is obviously a simplified representation of some significant items of information about me. The information in the care plan may be useful should someone need to look after me. The same information is presented in a completely different format in the life story example.

Care plan for Helen Hewitt

Eating and drinking:

- holds fork in left hand

- eats no animal products

Relationships:

- parents still alive

- has a brother and sister

- mother of two

- has a long-term partner

Occupation:

- part-time university lecturer and freelance life story consultant

Likes:

- exercise, especially running

- Spain and speaking Spanish

- salads and preparing vegetarian food

Example of a care plan

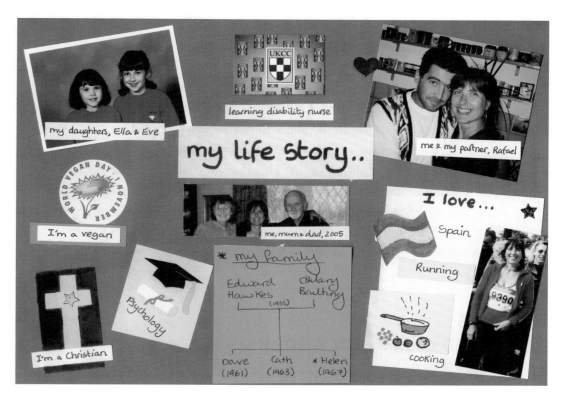

my life story..

learning disability nurse

my daughters, Ella & Eve

me & my partner, Rafael

WORLD VEGAN DAY 1 NOVEMBER

I'm a vegan

UKCC

me, mum & dad, 2005

Psychology

I'm a Christian

* my family

Edward Hawkes — Mary Boulting
(1955)

Dave   Cath   * Helen
(1961)   (1963)   (1967)

I love...

Spain

Running

cooking

9390

Example of a life story

Clearly there are differences in the two formats. The most striking is the visual impact of the life story version. It has an instant impact which requires no reading ability. It also sets out my life in terms of my relationships which could not be conveyed in the same way in a care plan. As previously stated, it is not the function of the care plan to do this. Another feature of the life story representation is that there is far more information available in the pictures. It is true that 'a picture paints a thousand words'. For example, it is not that I do not eat animal products for medical reasons, but the fact that I declare I am a vegan that says something about my values and philosophy of life. Also, by including a simple family tree you can see where I am placed within my family and how old I am. All in all, I think it is fair to say that you are more likely to feel you know me more from the life story version than the care plan. Of course this is greatly simplified, but gives a flavour of what impact a life story book can have.

A life story book does not have to be a book at all. As the above example illustrates, even a collage-style poster can be very powerful and informative. Life history information can be presented in all kinds of ways. It can be set out in a poster, scrap book, video or audio diary, or in computerised or specially adapted sensory enhanced versions for people with sensory impairments. All these variations will be considered later, but the emphasis is on the scrapbook type of life story book. Of course, the main thing to remember is that every life story project should be completely unique to the individual.

Exercise 2 - mapping out your own life story

It is extremely useful to reflect on your own life story before helping someone else with theirs. This will allow you to experience how the process affects you emotionally, which in turn will enable you to empathise with the other person. Jot down the key events and relationships from your past and present and gather some photographs. This does not have to be an exhaustive exercise – half a dozen pieces of information should suffice. You do not have to share this with anyone but if you do not want to discuss it with others ask yourself why. This will heighten your awareness of how important it is to be in control of what information others have access to about your personal life.

The value of life story books

In my unpublished Ph.D. thesis (1997) I explored the use of life story books for a group of people with profound learning disabilities moving from a long-stay hospital to a community home. During transitions such as these there is a risk that a person's stories and experiences, particularly regarding their relationships, could get lost. This is especially true if staff who have known the person for a number of years do not move with them.

Life story books were found to be useful tools for getting to know the person with learning disabilities, defining the person in wider terms than 'client' in the present, and displaying personality. They encouraged people to see the person as an individual with a unique life history (Hewitt, 1998; 2000; 2003). This moves beyond the parameters of a nursing care plan where the information about the person is purely of a clinical nature. Life story books can act as communication aids to assist in the initiation of therapeutic relationships.

Atkinson et al (2000) produced a book of stories by women with learning disabilities. All the women had specific issues they have had to cope with throughout their lives, including their identity as women with learning disabilities. The stories are told in their own words and provide valuable insight into their lives. Everyone can learn from these personal stories and appreciate how life is experienced by a person with learning disabilities.

Life story books also encourage people to make sense of events that have happened in the context of their life history (Bogdan and Taylor, 1994). This is particularly useful for people with complex needs who may have many issues they need to come to terms with. This includes traumatic events in their lives such as abusive relationships. However, due to the sensitivity of such information care needs to be taken to ensure the person has adequate support to address any issues that are brought to light. Life story books can also act as a resource for breaking down barriers between providers and users through encouraging mutual understanding. Most importantly, the person remains at the centre of the process. This is very pertinent in the light of the White Paper, as person-centred plans are the way forward in terms of care planning for each individual.

Chapter 2

Life story books for different client groups

Life story books can be used for all client groups. Identity is something that needs to be recognised in everyone, regardless of specific learning disabilities. This chapter presents case studies to illustrate how some very different individuals have made use of their life story books. Although names and details have been changed, all case studies are based on real people who have created or helped to compile their own life story books.

More able people

If a person can write their own life story book it can be a very valuable exercise in self-discovery. By revisiting the past a person can come to make sense of events and relationships within the context of their lifespan. It helps to encourage a sense of self by highlighting where they have come from and where they are now. If able to understand a sense of time, this can help the person to project into the future and consider things such as where they would like to live and work and who they want in their lives.

Bob

Bob is 51 and has lived in his own flat for the past seven years. Prior to this he lived in a large long-stay hospital for most of his life and also in a couple of small group homes. He has an older brother who is married with grown-up children. They have limited contact, two or three times a year, as they live over 100 miles apart.

Bob loves drawing and painting and has always had jobs involving this skill. Even at the hospital he used to help with maintenance, mainly painting and decorating.

He has also worked in craft-based workshops, producing goods for retail. Currently he works part-time in a co-operative scheme that makes furniture and gifts. Bob has a good circle of friends who he sees most Friday nights in the local pub. He also knows a couple of his neighbours quite well. There are many friends from his past who he has lost contact with.

Bob's life story book

On the days that Bob does not work he attends a local college. It was one of the tutors there who suggested that Bob compile a life story book. The idea was inspired by the fact that Bob is always talking about his past. Staff felt it would be an interesting project for him.

Bob discussed his ideas with one of the college staff. He wanted to contact some of the friends he had lived with in the hospital. There were also two members of staff, in particular, that he was very close to there. He was due to see his brother so compiled a set of questions to ask him. He sorted through a box of old photographs he wanted to include in his book and gathered some artefacts that were very special to him.

Initially Bob was helped to write his own memories and map the events and relationships throughout his life. He used all the photographs and memorabilia he had collected. Once he had done this he started to contact the other people for their stories and recollections. The whole process, to get the book up and running, took Bob two months. He spent more time decorating and adding to the book once he had collected information and written the main body of it.

Bob enjoyed reading his book over and over, and showed it to all his friends. He also went through it with his brother who was really moved by it. In fact, contact between them increased following the compilation of the book.

Older people

For older people a life story book can act as an aid to reminiscence. As we age our ability to remember often declines. As stated throughout this book our life history is essential to who we are as a person. Keeping the past alive helps us to maintain our identity while also allowing us to move forward. In later years it is even more important to have our recollections recorded because the older we get the less likely there will be others around us who share the same memories. This reduces the opportunity for discussing shared memories, so a resource such as a life story book can act as a tool for encouraging conversation about the person's life experiences.

For people with limited or declining communication skills a life story book can provide an account of their lives that would otherwise get lost. By being involved in the project the person can make sense of their past and relive the memories that have shaped who they are now. This can add to the person's sense of self-worth and give them a focused activity to engage in.

Albert

Albert is 68 years old and lives in a small group home with three other people. He is more than 20 years older than the other residents. Most of his life has been spent in a long-stay hospital and he has never been able to care for himself independently. He has lived in his current home for four years. The staff have observed a decline in Albert's ability to express himself and he has become increasingly withdrawn over the past year. He has no living relatives but is very close to the family of a previous carer.

When Albert lived in the hospital he used to deliver the post to all the departments. He was known throughout the hospital and enjoyed talking to everyone. Other than this Albert has never had a job. He attended day centres until three years ago when it was felt he was getting too old.

He used to be very agile and loved going for long walks in the country. He has always had an interest in nature, particularly birds and animals. It is currently difficult for him to go out as he now requires a wheelchair and gets tired very quickly. He still enjoys watching nature programmes on television and has many books and posters in his bedroom.

Albert's life story book

Staff in the house where Albert lives were aware that he was becoming less interactive with the other residents and staff. He would spend most of his day in an armchair not engaged in any activity. The staff had tried some new activities but with very limited response.

While some student nurses were on placement at the group home, one of them, Vicky, became close to Albert. She wanted to focus on him for her assignment which was concerned with life story books. Albert responded well to the one-to-one attention and began to engage more with the other people around him.

Through talking to Albert, Vicky managed to map out many relationships and events in Albert's life that were clearly important to him. He had very few photographs of the time he spent in the hospital, but Vicky accompanied him to the site and they took photographs of how it stands now. This visit also served to jog Albert's memory, as he recounted many stories.

Vicky also invited Albert's previous keyworker to contribute to his life story book. Albert knows the family well and they had photographs spanning many years. Once they had gathered the information they discussed how Albert would like to present his life story. He decided he wanted to make a poster to keep on his bedroom wall. This meant he could look at it whenever he wanted and could take people to his room to show them as and when he chose. His poster inspired the other people in the house to think about their own life stories and two of them have subsequently produced books.

People with challenging behaviour

Geoff

Geoff is 38 and lives in a secure residential setting with five other young men. He lived at home until he was 16 but his violence and physical strength became too much for his parents to cope with. They have maintained contact with Geoff and live close by. He has two younger sisters, both of whom visit him two or three times a year. He loves seeing his family and he sometimes visits his parents in their home.

Geoff has lived in many different residential settings over the years and has lived with many different people. Staff turnover is often high in these settings but he has had the same keyworker in two homes and is still with him now. Geoff takes antipsychotic medication and has weekly group therapy with a psychologist.

Due to Geoff's aggressive outbursts he does not have many personal belongings in his bedroom, but he does have free access to a secure hi-fi system which he uses daily. He loves music, particularly loud rap and rock music. The staff have accompanied him to a few music festivals which he thoroughly enjoyed. He also enjoys swimming and aromatherapy massage but only with people he feels comfortable with. Geoff's behaviour is always more challenging when there are changes taking place.

Geoff's life story book

The idea to compile a life story book with Geoff came from the weekly sessions he has with the psychologist. She felt there were issues that he could address through the process of telling his life story. Geoff responded positively to the suggestion. He was able to tell his own story so was the primary source of information for his book. He chose to involve his parents, sisters and keyworker. His psychologist co-ordinated the sessions.

Geoff was present for all the discussions about his life. These were recorded and Geoff kept the tapes to help him remember what had been said. The sessions were kept brief due to his short concentration span and tendency to get agitated if asked too many questions at one time. Although there were times during the process when he became agitated and visibly uncomfortable discussing certain events from his past, the psychologist was able to calm him by helping him to put the events in the context of his life history.

Geoff was in control throughout the process of compiling the life story book. He can write so was able to present the stories with little help. He just needed some guidance regarding the mapping out of stories in chronological order. Other than this he produced the book himself. He enjoyed compiling the book and keeps it with him and frequently shows people, and updates it regularly.

Of all the different client groups, people with challenging behaviour are probably the least understood. Often their reputation precedes them and can form a barrier to getting to know the person beneath the behaviour. If living in a care setting, most of the documentation about them is likely to be of a clinical or therapeutic nature and framed in the negative. To label someone problematic is very powerful and can overshadow the more positive and idiosyncratic characteristics of the person. It encourages carers to see the person in clinical and negative terms. This is no fault of the carers but there can be a huge void in the kind of information that focuses on the more human element of the person. In other words, the kinds of things that make up our identity (listed in chapter 1) are likely to be overlooked.

Another barrier to having access to this kind of information is that people with challenging behaviours are more likely to have experienced trauma in their lives. Painful events may be responsible for some or all of their current behaviour. Some people may feel it is too traumatic to compile a life story book based on events and experiences which are perceived as purely negative. However, this is making the assumption that the person cannot cope with their past and that it is better left unexplored. It may be that revisiting events in their life will help them to come to terms with them. As long as there is sufficient support on hand, the person can be guided through their life story in a safe environment.

People with profound learning disabilities

Many people with profound learning disabilities have difficulty communicating. This makes knowledge about their past difficult to share, often leaving huge gaps in their life history. Without this information it is harder to get to know the person and have a real sense of their identity. Filling in the gaps can help to enhance the person's identity and help to keep their past alive. More than the other client groups, people with profound learning disabilities will require complete assistance with compiling their life story books. To make the books as comprehensive and authentic as possible it will be necessary to include the accounts of third parties, in particular the person's immediate family or other relatives and any long-term relationships with friends and carers.

The person compiling the life story book needs to be aware of how much power they possess. It is a big responsibility presenting somebody else's life in a book. It is therefore useful to have support from other people who know the person as this helps to gauge the level of authenticity of the content of the book.

Jane

Jane is 38 years old and has very severe learning disabilities. She is the oldest of four children and lived at home for the first five years of her life. She then lived in a number of large care settings including two long-stay hospitals. Three years ago Jane moved into a new community home with five other people from the hospital where she lived.

Jane's parents maintained regular contact with her until two years ago when her father died. It has been very difficult for her mother to visit since his death, so contact has reduced considerably. Jane has lived with the same people for over 20 years but displays no signs of close friendships with anyone in particular. There is a fellow resident who has shared bedrooms with Jane and they have been on several holidays together, but Jane has remained visibly impartial, showing no observable signs of discrimination between the other people she lives with which makes it difficult to know who she views as a friend. She has had the same keyworker for over ten years and they have many shared memories.

It is difficult to determine what Jane's likes and dislikes are with certainty because of the nature of her disabilities. She is unable to state her preferences verbally and she does not display a large range of emotions. However, there are a couple of activities that have evoked a more consistent response from Jane. She appears to enjoy having a massage and being in the garden. She has always attended a day centre and engages in additional activities in the house.

Jane's life story book

The idea for Jane's life story book arose out of the transition from hospital to the community home where she currently lives. It was felt that such a transition posed a risk of losing information about Jane's life history and relationships. Her keyworker, Susan, and another carer decided to gather stories about Jane to put in a book that could be taken to her new home.

At the time, both Jane's parents were alive, so they were the first point of contact. Susan interviewed them and collected photographs spanning her whole life. One of Jane's siblings also agreed to discuss her memories so that they could be included in the book. Susan collated her own recollections and stories with those of Jane's family and other carers in the setting to produce a large scrapbook-style life story book. Susan showed it to Jane first and gauged her reaction before showing it to her family.

Once Jane had moved into the community home additions were made to the book to record the transition. Susan regularly reads the life story book to Jane, and it has made staff more aware of the need to record events and relationships important to the person.

Summary

This chapter has highlighted the variety of uses life story books can have for different client groups. Due to their individual nature they can be adapted to suit the needs of each person. The case studies illustrate the specific benefits for each client group: older people can use them as an aid to reminiscence; people with challenging behaviour can use the books to come to terms with traumatic events in their lives; and people with more profound learning disabilities can use their life story book to highlight and maintain their identity. The more able the person is the more direct input they can have in the process. However, all people can participate in the compilation of a life story book regardless of ability. Ways to encourage participation are discussed in chapter 4.

Chapter 3
Ethical considerations

Before even starting a life story project there are ethical issues that need to be considered. The four main ones addressed in this chapter are: consent, ownership, dealing with traumatic events and confidentiality. There are no hard and fast rules or right or wrong answers to these major issues. However, this chapter should alert you to the issues and guide you to address them prior to starting a life story book. The key word is sensitivity, as you need to remember that life story information is very personal and intimate and therefore needs to be treated with respect.

Consent

Consent is a vital part of any intervention that involves an individual in a care setting or research project. For people who fully understand the implications of any such intervention or research, consent is not normally a problem. They can express their desire to be part of the intervention or not. Often this would require a signature on a consent form. Sometimes verbal consent is adequate if witnessed by more than one person. However, consent is a major issue in the field of learning disabilities, particularly with people who have difficulty communicating. These people are considered to be 'vulnerable subjects' so require assistance to understand what is being asked of them.

Legal representation

People need to be deemed legally competent to participate in research or interventions in the care setting. A recently published EU Directive, *Medicines for Human Use (Clinical trials)* (2003), suggests that if a person is not legally competent then consent can be obtained from a 'legal representative'. This should be someone who is close to the person and who is expected to base their decision on the person's 'presumed will'.

For the purpose of gaining consent to participate in a life story book project a close relative is the most appropriate legal representative if the person is unable to give consent.

Consent should always be:

- voluntary

- informed

- in writing

Each of these is considered in turn below, followed by a section on legal representation in the case of people who are unable to give their own consent.

Consent should be voluntary

People should give their consent willingly and not be coerced into it. This can be difficult with people with learning disabilities, even if they can communicate verbally, as they may be easily influenced. Consent for involvement in a life story project is different from other kinds of intervention or research as the output of the project is purely for the benefit of the person. They will go on to own the book and it will be for their use only. This needs to be made clear from the start.

Consent should be informed

For consent to be informed the potential participants need to be given sufficient information, in a format they understand, to enable them to make a decision whether or not to participate in the intervention. This presents the major problem when trying to obtain consent from people with learning disabilities. It is essential that information is pitched at the appropriate level for each individual. You may need to develop a picture board with symbols if this is the system that the person is familiar with. The Department of Health produced a leaflet in 2001 about consent aimed at people with learning disabilities. They use symbols and describe the process involved in giving consent to medical procedures when visiting the doctor or hospital. This leaflet could easily be adapted to inform the person about involvement in a life story project. The key element is making it meaningful for the individual to maximise their understanding of what is expected of them. They should also be given the opportunity to change their mind at any time.

It is useful to have an example of a completed book or sample pages to show the person. Again, this needs to be with the consent of the owner. You can copy pages from this book or compile a brief life history of yourself (like my own presented in chapter 1) to illustrate what a life story book is. Only when the person is aware of what is involved can they make an informed decision. Although many benefits of having a life story book are highlighted throughout this book not everybody will want to have one about their own life. It is important to keep this in mind.

After presenting the relevant information, time should be given for the person to reflect on what they are being asked. They may rush into a decision, either way, and regret it later. For example, some people who are shy and take a long time to build trust with others may immediately decline to take part in a life story project but later see the benefits of compiling a book on their life. Likewise, some people may eagerly agree with the idea but later feel unsure whether they want to proceed. A cooling off period will help the person to make the decision that feels right for them.

Consent should be in writing

It is always preferable to have written consent where possible. Again, this is likely to be difficult for people with learning disabilities. Only a minority of people will be able to write, although some may be able to make a mark on a form provided they understand what they are signing and that it is witnessed. Likewise, in the case of people who are unable to provide written consent, verbal consent in the presence of witnesses is acceptable.

If written consent is achievable then two copies are needed. One should remain with the person and the other should be kept for reference in case the issue of consent is raised at a later date. For example, if a relative visits and sees a life story book they may feel that elements of it are too intimate or personal and may question whether the person gave permission to use the information. Consent is primarily to protect the individual, which is why it is essential that it is informed and documented.

Ownership

Another important issue to be addressed at the outset of a life story project is ownership. It needs to be clear to everyone living and working with the individual that the completed book is the property of that person. It is essential that a life story book does not take on a care planning function and be kept with other documentation about the person. Although life story books can be very useful in the process of person-centred planning they should be used alongside the person and not the care plan. The individual whose book it is should always be in control of who has access to their book.

For people with less severe disabilities this is easier to address. Talking to the person will establish how they want their book to be used. Some people may decide that they want to keep it in the lounge among other personal items such as photograph albums and may be happy for everyone to have access to their life story book. Other people may prefer to keep the book in a more personal space such as their bedroom and determine who has access to the book.

People with more severe learning disabilities will need to be helped to keep their life story book in a place that respects their privacy. Their bedroom, a personal bag or their wheelchair may be the appropriate place. The key thing to remember is that life story books are personal artefacts that often contain very intimate details of an individual's life and therefore need to be treated with respect and sensitivity.

Traumatic events

The third ethical issue that needs attention prior to embarking on a life story project is the handling of traumatic events. This will not affect everyone, but, until you start delving, a person's past is a complete unknown and may therefore bring up some disturbing memories. It is essential that you are prepared literally for anything. This is why it is important that the person helping with the life story book is well known to the individual, so that they feel safe when sharing the intimate details of their life history.

Regardless of the person's disabilities, if you are helping them with their life story book you are in a position of responsibility. Whatever life events are discussed you should always be alert to the reactions of the person. If you feel there is a likelihood that a negative reaction may occur it is important that you have some back-up in place. This may be a family member who can console them through difficult memories, or a more senior staff member with experience of managing emotional difficulties. For example, someone with counselling experience should be able to debrief both the individual and the helper, to bring the person back to the present and put the memories into context.

Reassurance is an essential part of the helper's role. You may need to keep reassuring the person that what they are recounting is positive, even if it feels painful for them at times. You need to help them to bear in mind the potential benefits of confronting difficult issues, that they will ultimately be able to make sense of these events within the context of their life history.

If you find that the person you are helping is experiencing immense emotional trauma by recalling events from their past you will have to decide, between you, whether it is productive to continue with the project. If severely affected by the activity, it may be necessary to seek the advice of a clinical psychologist or psychiatrist. It is unlikely that you will need to do this, but it is always better to be prepared. The decision to stop should be made by the person, but you will need to use your discretion as to whether you think they are capable of making that decision. It does not have to be an all or nothing type of activity. You may decide to shelve the project for a while until the person feels strong enough to continue, or you could choose to focus on the more positive aspects of their life.

Sometimes it is the effect on you as a helper that may be more difficult to control than the response of the person. For example, it may be that the person recounts events in their life in a matter of fact manner, but something, such as a questionable encounter with a relative or member of staff, may strike you as disturbing. There are various ways in which you can manage this situation. First of all, you will need to be clear what it is the person is describing. If you feel there is a chance that some form of abuse has occurred you will need to be sure that the person understands the implications of this. Do not act hastily as it may be that the person has problems expressing themself and has merely described an event or relationship in a manner that appears suspicious. Likewise, they may have embellished the truth, so it is not appropriate to act straight away. Discuss any concerns you have with the person and seek clarification. Only then will you be in a position to act. Clearly, you need to be guided by the person. If they are not concerned there is little you can do about it except, if appropriate, to encourage them to censor certain parts of their life story book.

If you feel out of your depth you should seek support. This may be from a relative of the person or a member of staff who is well known to them. Two or more heads are better than one when it comes to dealing with issues of a delicate nature. The key word, again, is sensitivity. Each situation will be unique and should be treated as such. There are no right or wrong answers to these scenarios. Just use your common sense, be sensitive and keep everything in proportion. Does the emergence of a difficult memory justify the abolition of the life story book? With the appropriate help and support most situations can be managed to a positive solution. Wherever possible the person should remain in control of the process and it should be for them to decide what and how memories are recounted in their life story book.

Confidentiality

It should go without saying that whatever you discuss with people during the compilation of a life story book must be treated in strict confidence. If tape recordings are used during interviews they must be returned to the person or destroyed once the information has been extracted. In certain instances, in discussion with the person, it may be decided that a pseudonym be used for a certain person or people in their life if they do not wish their identity to be known.

Confidentiality is central to all codes of professional conduct within the health and social care professions, so it should be second nature to carers within their practice. However, carers are also responsible for extending this code of conduct to other personnel and visitors to the setting. If anyone views a life story book, even with the permission of the owner, they should be alerted to the confidential nature of the information they have read. This is probably the only resemblance that a life story book has to any other nursing documentation about the person in the care setting.

Summary

This chapter has highlighted some of the ethical issues which need to be addressed before embarking on a life story project. These include making sure you have appropriate consent either from the person or a legal representative, ensuring the ownership of the book remains with the person, managing traumatic events in a safe and appropriate manner, and ensuring that everyone connected to the project respects the confidential nature of the information. Ethics are not always black and white and as such each case must be dealt with on an individual basis. Think how you would like others around you to treat personal and intimate details about your life. The key word to remember is 'sensitivity'.

Chapter 4

Encouraging participation

It is essential to ensure that the person with learning disabilities retains as much control as possible over the compilation of their life story book. Sometimes this can be difficult, especially if the person has severe or profound disabilities. It is the aim of this chapter to demonstrate the ways in which you can maximise the opportunities for participation, regardless of disabilities – in other words, make the process as user friendly as possible. This goes from introducing and explaining the idea through to actually compiling their book.

Introducing the idea

Telling stories about our lives and who we are is part of everyday life for most of us. It is how we relate to others and make sense of the events that unfold in time. However, the concept of life history or biography can be difficult for people with learning disabilities to grasp. Generally they won't have been encouraged to tell their stories, although this should now be changing in the light of contemporary philosophies of care which encourage inclusion and person-centred approaches to care. There has been a noticeable increase in the number of published accounts written by or for people with learning disabilities. See chapter 1 for references.

In order to explain the past it is first necessary to understand the present. You can help the person get a sense of the present by drawing a time line. Put today in the middle and leave spaces to add pictures. Any time prior to today will appear to the left of centre and any time beyond to the right. Using an instant Polaroid or digital camera is a great way of surveying the present before exploring the past. If possible let the person take photographs of anything they choose from the present time. They will then see the results instantly and this can be stuck in the middle of the time line. A couple of old photographs can be stuck to the left. The future is a much harder concept to grasp, and may confuse the person. It is not essential for them to understand this in order to comprehend the notion of a life story book. It is far more important to make a connection with their past and the present.

Once you have helped to explain what a life story book is it is very useful to show the person an example, especially if it is of someone the person already knows. This will have much more meaning to them. Even if the person cannot talk, go through the book with them, highlighting photographs and the overall presentation of the book. It can act as a template for their own book.

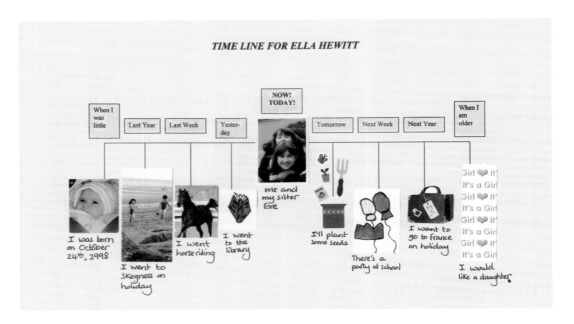

Example of a time line

Gauging reaction

The single most important aspect of encouraging the participation of the person is the ability to gauge their reaction to the information being discussed or presented. Sometimes this will be quite blatant, especially if the person can articulate their opinions. Even if they do not use words, some people can express themselves very effectively using gestures, facial expressions and other body language. With some people, however, it will be far more difficult to know what they think about any given information presented to them. This is where the relationship between the person and the helper is crucial. Trust only comes from knowing the person and feeling safe in their presence, which all takes time to foster. The more you know the person the more likely you are to be able to read their expressions and 'best guess' their opinions. You may not always be right but you need to use all the cues available to encourage the individual to participate.

Even if a person cannot contribute physically to the compilation of their book, their presence can be made conspicuous by recording their reactions. For example, once the book has been compiled make sure it is read to the person first. Watch carefully as the book is read and gauge any reactions. It may be that a particular story made the person smile or a certain photograph engaged the person more than others. These observations are crucial and they need to be written up and added to the book. An example is given below.

Lance's laughter

Following a story about a family holiday where Lance's father fell out of a boat, Lance laughed. When read to him on several other occasions he responded in the same way. So, as part of this story, Lance's reaction was included by adding, 'every time Lance hears this story he laughs'.

This sensitivity to reaction will be what makes the book feel more like it belongs to the person than merely another document about them. It may be the only way to feel their presence in the book. So never think that because a person cannot talk and has very severe physical disabilities they cannot contribute to the creation of their own life story.

Discussing content

Once the person has an idea of what a life story book is, the next step is to decide what they would like to include. The level of participation at this stage will vary greatly according to the person's level of comprehension and communication. It is a good idea to use the example life story book to highlight themes and ideas. These may include:

- a family tree diagram
- photographs from all stages of the person's life
- photographs of activities, groups and residential settings the person has been part of
- photographs of family, friends and other key people
- souvenirs from holidays
- artwork and other personal work
- certificates

If the person has limited communication skills it is likely that you will be gathering the information and writing it up yourself. However, it is essential to keep in mind that the person should always remain at the centre of the process. If they cannot talk, the above list is one way of trying to engage them in planning what to include in their book. Use the person's physical and expressed emotional reactions to guide you through this stage.

Targeting informants

Another part of the planning stage is drawing up a list of people who you want to contribute to the book. Some people with learning disabilities will be able to do this easily and may even be able to contact the people on the list directly. More information about approaching contributors is presented in chapter 5.

For people requiring more help this is where photographs and other audio-visual materials help. Showing some home videos and looking through photograph albums can help the person identify the key people in their lives. Even if they do not want all these people to contribute personally they may still want to include them in their own stories.

The importance of pride

When creating anything we nearly always experience some level of pride. We may feel proud for reaching a deadline at work or get a sense of satisfaction for having painted the lounge. Sometimes this feeling is accompanied by a sense of disbelief that you actually performed to a level that you did not think possible. This feeling of pride helps to raise our self-esteem which makes us feel good about ourselves.

People with learning disabilities often have low self-esteem. They may not have been given opportunities in the past to experience the feeling of pride that comes with independence, even at a very low level such as being able to put their own arm in the sleeve of their jumper. This is particularly true of people who have had things done to them throughout their lives.

Compiling a life story book can help raise a person's self-esteem because the book is purely about them. Encouraging participation, at any level, will help the person to put their own stamp on their life story. We should never underestimate how valuable this sense of pride is for our personal growth and development.

Hands-on participation

Wherever possible you should encourage the person to be involved in the compilation of their life story book. In chapter 2 examples were given for people with very different disabilities, from Bob who could write his own book to Jane whose book was written almost solely by someone else.

Recording memories

If a person has a sense of what they want to include in their life story book they should be encouraged to record these memories. Some people may be able to write the memories down. Other people might find it useful to verbalise their memories and record them on a tape recorder which is very useful as it can be played back any number of times.

Disposable cameras

Disposable cameras are a very cheap and easy way to gather photographs of people and places currently pertinent in the person's life. If possible give them the camera and let them take photographs of what and whom they want. If they cannot take the photographs themselves you can take some and discuss which ones they want to include. For people with more profound learning disabilities you will have to use your skills in reading their reactions to decide which photographs to use.

Artwork and gluing

Wherever possible you should include any pictures, paintings or other work produced by the person. This is a way of keeping them at the centre of the book and increasing their sense of pride and self-esteem. It is always nice to show off work we are proud of and a life story book is an ideal place to do this.

Sticking photographs or other artefacts is an activity that most people can engage in. Even if you have to write most of the life story book yourself, the person can be involved in the actual physical compilation of the book by gluing things in and seeing the book take shape.

Summary

This chapter has highlighted both the importance of participation and how this can be encouraged at every stage of the life story process. Even people with very profound learning disabilities can be encouraged to participate at some level, ensuring that their presence is not lost from the book itself.

Chapter 5

Getting started

Starting a life story book is probably quite a daunting prospect for most people. The first myth to dispel is that collecting information for a life story book is arduous and time consuming. There is no doubt that it can be, but only if you choose to make it so. A life story book can be up and running in no time. Remember that you do not have to treat it as a complete biography, telling the whole story of a person's life. In the first instance, you should be aiming for the skeleton of the person's life, which can be fleshed out later. Life story books are an evolving resource which should be added to in order to maximise their benefit. The aim of this chapter is to motivate you to get started on a life story project.

Making contacts

People who require little assistance

If the person is able to write their own life story book, then obviously they will be the prime source of information. They may decide not to include other people's accounts. Even if they are very able they may still require some assistance with putting the book together. They should be encouraged to choose someone they trust to help them. It is essential that it is someone who will honour their decisions regarding what they want to include and leave out of their book. If it is someone too close they may have very strong opinions regarding the events being reported. They may even feature a lot throughout the stories. This can be a very positive experience, as they can share the memories and produce an enhanced account of these events. What you need to avoid, however, is allowing the third party to take over the project and put their own slant on the stories.

As the person remembers more and more stories for their book, they may want to contact certain people who were part of their past. It is helpful to write a list of these people as they think of them. If they no longer know where they live or work ask around as it is likely that someone knows where they are.

When you do contact the person try and be clear about what it is you want from them. It is good to have a short summary of the aim of the life story book, along with the specific memory you want the person to comment on. An example is given below.

Example description of life story book and invitation to participate

I am writing a life story book. It is a book about my life with lots of stories and memories from my past and present. I would like to include some stories from you, of the time we spent together.

The person may be able to identify specific events they want the contact person to write about or they may want to just give them the freedom to write whatever they choose. Remind them that they do not have to include anything they are not happy with.

To summarise, go through the following questions with the person you are helping.

- Does the person need help with their life story book?

- If yes, who do they trust to help them?

- Do they want to include anyone else in their book?

- If so, who?

- Do we know how to contact these people?

- If not, who can help us to find them?

- Once we make contact do we know what we want from them?

People who require more support

If you are compiling a life story book on behalf of someone who requires a lot of support, there are further questions and issues you will need to consider. The person you are helping should be your primary source of information. If they have difficulty communicating you will need to extend your sources beyond. However, try as far as possible to involve the person right from the start (see chapter 4).

If you know the person well already it is likely that you will also know the significant people in their lives. This will make your task much easier when it comes to approaching suitable contacts. Do not worry if you can only think of one or two possible sources. It is amazing how much information one other person can provide, especially if they are a close family member who has known the person all their life. Also, it is likely that each source you identify will know of at least one other person who could contribute. This way you end up with a trail of contacts and a network of people who can say something about the life of the person you are helping.

Before you make contact with anyone you should be clear about what the aims of the life story book are. Talking about someone's life can be very intimate and sensitive and this must always be borne in mind. Whereas we find it relatively easy to discuss personal details about our lives on a daily basis and are able to discriminate who we tell what, carers and relatives may find this very difficult. They need to be assured that they fully understand what is being asked of them and that they believe it is in the best interest of the relative or person in their care. This means you need to build a trusting relationship with all the people you approach regarding the life story of the person you are helping.

It is a good idea for you to have a 'story' for the life story book project yourself. Write this down so you are clear at all times why you are embarking on this task and the benefits for the person. It will help tremendously when it comes to inviting people to participate. An example is given below.

Example of the reasons and aims for compiling a life story book for Johnny

I am helping Johnny to write a life story book because he is going to move to a community home soon. He will be leaving the friends and carers he has known for over 20 years. His parents are getting very old and it would be sad for them to die without documenting some of the stories they have of Johnny throughout his life. Because Johnny cannot speak, he will never be able to talk about his experiences. A life story book will be a personal record of some of the experiences Johnny has had which may otherwise go undocumented. It is a way of keeping his past alive when he moves to a new home, providing continuity of his identity.

As you are close to Johnny, I thought you might like to contribute to his life story book. Any stories or salient memories of your time together, including some photographs, would add such a lot to his book.

I would like to discuss this further so if you have any questions do not hesitate to contact me.

[Sign your name and state your association to Johnny. Add contact details.]

Tips for making contacts

If the person with a learning disability lives at home with the family:

- Approach the family first.
- Either send a letter detailing the aims of the life story book or discuss personally using the contents of the letter. The family can keep this to refer to in their own time.
- If there is a third party who knows the family better than you do, ask them to make the initial contact.
- Respect the wishes of the family even if they decline to take part in the process. They may change their mind later.
- Be sure the family understands what is being asked of them in terms of input to the life story book.
- If the family supports the project, allow them to take control as much as possible. This will reinforce the trust and respect between you. Remember, this may be the first time they have been given the chance to be the 'expert' on their relative, so be a captive audience.

If the person lives in a residential setting:

- Talk to the carers who know the person best.

- Draw up a list of suitable contacts between you. This will include:
  - known family members
  - friends of the person who can communicate verbally
  - current carers
  - previous carers who were close to the person

- Approach each contact, being clear of your aims for compiling the book and exactly what is being asked of them.

Once you have made the initial contact you will need to gauge the reaction of the contributor. You have to respect their wishes if they decide not to participate. There are many possible reasons for such a decision, all of which are very sensitive. It may just be too painful and difficult for a family member to recount the past. Often there will be a degree of guilt and this can be hard for some people to reconcile. However, by participating in the life story process these feelings can be worked through just by recounting memories and putting them into context. For example, most parents will feel guilty about handing over the care of their child. By telling their story they can remind themselves of the circumstances that led to that decision and also how their child's life has progressed since that time. Most people will have developed friendships in the places they have lived and some will have become more independent in some areas of their everyday life. The acknowledgement of this fact can help to ease some of the guilt that parents feel.

Other sources of information

The primary source of information will be the life story interviews with relevant informants. However, there are other sources of information that can enhance a life story book. Some of these are summarised below. Make a check list to ease the task of gathering information. It should be made as user friendly as possible, according to the needs of the individual. Symbols may help the person to understand what is useful to include in their book.

Material to include in a life story book can be any of the following:

- **Birth certificate:** This can set the scene for the person's life story and provides interesting information regarding place of birth and parental occupations at the time of the person's birth.

- **Postcards:** These may be of places the person has visited or cards received from family or friends.

- **Certificates:** Most people are proud of certificates and a life story book is an appropriate place to present them.

- **Magazine cuttings:** These can be of things the person values, such as idols or articles of interest.

- **Drawings:** It is always nice to include personal work from the individual. Where a person is unable to write their own book this is even more important. Drawings can be an expression of self and add a lot to a life story book.

- **Poems:** Personal work is invaluable and if a person can write poetry it would really enhance their life story book.

- **Letters:** Like postcards, letters are a good way of keeping the memories of special relationships alive by including them in the life story book.

- **Audio and video cassettes:** Sometimes it is helpful to have recordings of the person. Like photographs they provide a snapshot of a person at any one point in time. These recordings are particularly useful where the person is getting older and may be losing some of their faculties. Playing the tapes to them can help them to remember the things they have done and the people who may no longer be in their lives. This can be an easier way to absorb information. Retaining the life story interviews is a perfect use of these.

To get you in the mood

The exercise below is a useful way of preparing you for the next stage of the life story process – collecting information through interviews. This can be quite daunting, but the exercise allows you to role play in a safe environment before the actual event.

Exercise 3 - role play

You will need either three or four participants for this exercise. Each of you should assume one of the following roles:

- interviewer
- parent
- carer (from care setting)
- person with learning disabilities

If there are only three participants exclude the carer role.

The interviewer will need to be separated from the rest of the group initially. Take 20 to 30 minutes to prepare for the exercise. Interviewers will need this time for devising their interview schedule. The other participants will need to devise a persona and brief history of the person whose life story is being explored.

Once everyone is happy with their role begin the life story interview. The interviewer will need to take notes. Take 30 to 45 minutes for the actual interview. At the end give the information you have gathered to a third party, introducing the person whose life story you have heard. This should seem quite real.

This exercise should demonstrate how easy it is to gather sufficient information to make a significant start on a life story project.

Summary

The aim of this chapter has been to motivate you to start a life story project. Do not go into it feeling it is going to be too difficult and complicated because this will prevent you from making a start. Remember, you do not need to write every detail of a person's life history. One or two interviews and a few photographs are all it takes to get a book up and running. From that point they can be added to as they are an evolving resource that is never complete.

By this stage you should have a list of suitable contacts, an idea of how you can approach them and ideas for supplementary information to include in the book. The next chapter examines ways in which this information can be collected.

Chapter 6
Collecting information

Once you are motivated to start a life story book and you have approached the people who are going to contribute, you will need to consider how you are going to collect information from these people. The aim of this chapter is to highlight the steps necessary for gathering information for a life story book. There is no one right way to compile a life story book but there are useful tips that will help you to collect sufficient information to form the basis of the book.

Preparing for the life story interviews

Once your contacts have agreed to take part in the compilation of the life story book you will need to prepare for an interview with them so that you record the relevant information for inclusion in the book. As stated in chapter 5, it is advisable to have a recording device such as a tape recorder, video or mini disc recorder. This makes life much easier when talking to people. However, trying to write down what is being said during the interview can interfere with the flow of the conversation and a lot of information can get lost. You should always inform people you are going to record the interview and give them the opportunity to decline but it is important that they realise the benefits of recording and that the material will be kept safe and confidential. If they are self-conscious these effects wear off very quickly once they are into the flow of conversation.

Before any interviews are carried out make sure you have primed the interviewees thoroughly. You should have notified them by letter (such as the example in chapter 5), or verbally, explaining the aims of the life story book. Before arranging a time and place for an interview ask the contact to collect any photographs or memorabilia that have specific meaning to them.

Devising an interview schedule

There is no definitive list of questions you need to have before starting a life story interview. Each interview situation will be unique and bring up issues specific to the individual. However, some themes are useful for guiding the interview. It is very difficult to start an interview cold, so having a list of loose questions will help to get the interview up and running. A schedule will also reduce the chance of too many digressions, as it is easy for interviews to drift.

The following is a list of questions that I find useful as a starting point when talking to family members. You can add questions relating to specific areas of an individual's life as appropriate. For example, if they are of a certain ethnic origin or religious persuasion you may want to find out more about this.

Simple interview schedule for interviewing the person with learning disabilities

If the person is unable to write their own stories, or has difficulty organising their thoughts coherently, you will need to help them decide what they want to include in their life story book. It is essential that you keep the questions brief and simple. According to the person's level of understanding and communication style you may need to adapt the schedule. Obviously, this will be done on an individual basis, but the following categories may be a good starting point:

- family members

- places they have lived

- friends (past and present)

- favourite pastimes

- holidays they have had

- dreams and aspirations

Simple interview schedule for family members

- birth story (where, when and how born, including birth weight)
- family structure (get a fuller picture of how the person fits into their family)
- how the person was as a baby and young child
- relationships with other family members
- help the family received when the person lived at home
- the effect on the whole family
- places where the person has been cared for (including day care, respite and residential)
- particular happy memories
- significant events in the person's life
- special objects or toys the person had as a child
- relationships with other people (eg friends, neighbours, shopkeepers, etc)
- holiday stories (memories of holidays over the years)
- family members or friends who could contribute to the book

The list may need to be altered according to the person's specific situation. Try and find out some background before you are faced with the actual interview. This is not always possible but can reduce the chance of asking questions that cause unnecessary anxiety. For example, if you know the person never lived at home it is pointless and insensitive to ask questions about home life.

Below are some of the stories that carers and other non-family members can contribute to a life story book. They will have been primed to bring along some photographs that have significance to them, so these will help to organise the interview.

Simple interview schedule for non-family members

- When did you first meet the person?

- Where were they living at the time?

- What was your connection with them?

- What are your earliest memories of your time together?

- What special memories do you have of the person?

- Describe what the person was like then and now. How have they changed?

- Do you have any holiday memories?

- Talk through your photographs.

- Are there any other people you think would be a good contact for telling stories about the person?

You will probably find that once the interview is up and running you will not need to consult your schedule. When interviewees are in full flow, it is likely that they will tell you far more than what you have prepared on your list of questions. However, not everyone is so articulate or talkative, so the schedule will provide prompts to continue the interview if there are awkward silences.

Checking your recording equipment

Once you have your interview schedule and you are in the interview situation you need to have recording equipment that is in good working order. From personal experience I have found that many things can go wrong at this stage. To prevent this from happening I have devised a checklist below.

Some essential advice when using recording equipment

- Always check that it works prior to the interview.

- Make sure you have spare batteries in case they run out during the session.

- Use a clean tape each time to avoid erasing previously recorded material.

- Listen out for when it is time to turn the tape over or you may lose valuable stories if the machine has switched itself off.

- Do a sound check to make sure it is positioned in a suitable location. It is extremely frustrating to play back a tape and not be able to hear the speakers.

Conducting the interview

Putting people at ease

You will need to negotiate with the interviewees where the best place to hold the interview would be. Some people feel happier in their own homes, whereas others like to come to an office (either in the place where the person lives or your place of work if this is different).

Try and make the atmosphere as informal as possible. Make sure that the person whose book it is has someone they trust with them. It can be very threatening and intimidating being asked personal questions if the person does not feel comfortable with the interviewer. This is also true of parents and other relatives who may not be used to this kind of interviewing. They, too, need to feel at ease to talk about events and memories that are very personal to them.

A good way to get things started is to reiterate what was said on the invitation letter. This is the schedule described above which sets things out clearly, so everyone knows what is expected of them.

The fact that you will be recording the interview may cause some initial anxiety. Reassure the participants that it will only be used for ease of collecting information without having to write everything down and that no one else will have access to the contents. Confidentiality is paramount. If the equipment is already running when the interviewee comes in, by the time you have exchanged pleasantries and the interview starts they will normally forget it is there.

Over to them

People requiring little support will be able to conduct the interview themselves. You will be there to prompt where necessary to keep the flow of the interview going.

The most important thing to remember is to let the person take the lead wherever possible. This goes for the person whose book it is but equally for family members too. It may be the first time they have been asked for this kind of information. There will be hundreds of personal stories and memories that they have about their relative, and normally people really appreciate having a captive audience for these stories. It is an opportunity for them to be the 'expert' for once, so respect this and allow them to say whatever they want. By recording the interview you can always play it back later for the content, so give your full attention while the person is talking. Equally, this kind of platform can be intimidating for some people, so be prepared to help out by asking leading questions if they are slow to open up. These can be taken from the interview schedule, such as the example presented earlier.

So be attentive and express interest in what is being said. Your role is more one of facilitator than interviewer, guiding the person through their memories. It is amazing how much information can be shared in a single interview. You are likely to learn a great deal from these conversations even if you have known the person for a number of years.

Interviews with multiple participants

How the life story interviews are conducted will depend on many factors. The most important one is the preference of the person whose book it is. They may want to talk to each informant on an individual basis. This does tend to work best, as people are then afforded the opportunity to talk openly about their individual memories. However, sometimes it can be appropriate to invite more than one participant to the interview. An example is if a person's keyworker knows the relevant family member very well. They can share experiences and put each other at ease. Having multiple participants also reduces the time it takes to collect information as you are likely to capture more stories in one session.

If there are more than one or two participants in the interview you may need to ensure that no one person dominates the conversation. Let the person whose book it is take the lead where this is possible.

Dealing with sensitive issues

Sometimes people will tell you things that are controversial or extremely sensitive, for example allegations of abuse or maltreatment in previous care settings or inappropriate sexual encounters. It is important to listen to what is being said then ask if the person wants the information to be used. This will need to be negotiated at the time of the interview so it is clear how the issues are to be treated. If the person cannot speak up for themself, their relatives will need to decide how to express the events, if at all. It will depend how significant these events are and how important it is to the person that they include them. They are likely to be part of what has shaped the person into who they currently are, so glossing over them may not be desirable. Also, by addressing them it can help the person to come to terms with traumatic events in their life.

For more information on this issue see chapter 3 on ethical considerations.

The use of photographs

Photographs are a very useful tool in a life story interview. Having asked participants to bring significant photographs with them, they will usually have the relevant stories in the forefront of their minds. You can literally conduct the whole interview around the selection of photographs available. If the interview slows down or dries up, just pick another photograph up as a prompt to another story.

Make sure you get as much information as possible from each photograph. Dates and names of people and places will enhance the story. Photographs are precious so reassure people that you will copy them so they can have the originals back. It is easy to scan photographs on most personal computers, or you can take them to a photographic shop to have them copied.

Ending the interview

There is no set limit to how long a life story interview should last. Some people can talk and talk, others have a more concise style of storytelling, but most people will dry up between one to two hours. A useful guide and prompt is when the tape recorder switches off. This will depend on the length of tape you are using, but ninety minutes is a suitable length of time. If people really are in the flow you can ask if they want to carry on or return for a second session.

When closing the interview it is important that you explain the next step to the participants. This is what you are going to do with the information they have supplied. They must be happy with this. In the case of multiple participant interviews, people other than family members must appreciate that anything they have heard during an interview should be treated in the strictest confidence. Explain that you will write up their recollections into stories and will show these to them before formalising them into a life story book. It is important that they realise they have the power to accept or reject any story that you shape out of the interviews. Remember that they are in control of the process. You are merely facilitating it.

Storing the information

Once you have collected your information from the life story interviews it is essential that you store it safely. Firstly, this is to ensure confidentiality, as the nature of the material is very personal. However, equally important is the fact that this information is invaluable as it will form the basis of the book you are facilitating.

This means you will need to make sure that none of it is lost. It is a good idea to have back-up copies of the tapes used for the interviews. It is also advisable to play the tapes back as soon as possible and take detailed notes from them. This way you will have a hard copy of the interviews should anything happen to the tapes.

Summary

This chapter has provided practical advice for collecting information for a life story book. In the first instance this can be achieved by one or two interviews with relevant people. These interviews can yield volumes of material which is often enough to make a substantial start on a book. The most important thing to remember is to let the participants take as much control of the process as possible. You are there to facilitate, although in some cases this will involve far more control. Always be aware of this and respect the wishes of the people involved.

Chapter 7

Presenting a life history

Once you have gathered the information you want to include in the life story book the next stage is to interpret and present the information. The message throughout this book is that there is no one right way to produce a life story book and it is the aim of this chapter to illustrate the many variations possible. There are, however, some general guidelines and pieces of advice given below which will be useful regardless of the type of presentation chosen.

Most of this chapter is devoted to tips for compiling a scrapbook-style life story book but other ways of presenting life story information are also illustrated with examples.

Their life in your hands

In some ways collecting the information for a life story book is the easier task. Once you have this information you have to make decisions regarding how it is to be presented. This is a big responsibility as the presentation will inevitably affect how the book is received and interpreted. If the person is able to present the information themself your input should be minimal and you should assume the role of facilitator. If, however, the person needs more help with the compilation of their life story book you will need to keep in mind the impact you can have on how others view the person. This should not put you off being involved in a life story project. On the contrary, it can be seen as an opportunity to really highlight all the identity-rich information and experiences the person has had which would otherwise go unrecorded. See it as a privilege to have this opportunity to present the person as a unique individual. It may be the first time in their life that this is done. With any privilege there is the risk of abuse or the temptation to take over and put your own perspective on the stories. This is especially true if someone close to the person, such as a keyworker, is responsible for writing the stories. Remember the advice given in chapter 4 about keeping the person at the centre of the life story.

Compiling a life story book

Regardless of how much information you have gathered during the life story interviews, the next stage involves reducing this information to a series of stories or episodes in the person's life. This is where you have to be selective about what goes into the life story book and, equally important, what gets left out. You should try to retain as much authenticity as possible which involves trying to convey the stories as near to how they were told to you as possible.

Feedback from source

Before writing the final version of the stories it is essential that you report back to their source for verification. This may be the person themselves, a relative or friend. Show them your condensed version of their stories and take note of their feedback. They may decide that they do not want to include certain things or may want to elaborate on others.

The time that elapses between the interview and feedback gives both you and the original source time to digest what has been discussed and may spark off other stories to include. It is also an opportunity to think of other participants to approach. Once everyone is happy that the version of their stories you have written is acceptable you will then have the main subject matter for the life story book.

Layout

When compiling a life story book of the scrapbook kind it is preferable to present the stories in a loose-leaf folder so that stories can be added to at any stage and not just at the back of the book. For example, if a relative visits who has not seen the person for a number of years they may recall stories from the distant past. These can then be jotted down and added at the relevant juncture. Stories can be written on coloured card and put in protective transparent pockets to prolong their life.

There are no hard and fast rules when it comes to compiling a life story book, but you may want to create some kind of order to the stories you have collected. The most obvious way is to present the information in chronological order. If you have been able to interview a parent it is likely that they will have described the birth of their child. This makes a very interesting start to a person's life story, although it may not always be possible to have such information. Even if you have only managed to trace a person's life back to the place they lived prior to the current setting it still makes sense to start the book at the earliest date traced. As long as you have information from before this day you have the basis of a life history, and tomorrow today will be history so it's never too late to make a start.

Additions should be encouraged at any stage so that the books are not seen as complete documents. One way of encouraging this is to place a note on the back page of the book, such as: 'Life story books are never complete. Add to this one whenever possible and appropriate. Record any stories told by carers or relatives.'

Carers need to get into the habit of making additions to the books whenever something noteworthy happens. For example, a holiday or special event attended, or a story conveyed by a family member relating to the person's past. Often these stories are only shared between two or three people who happen to be present at the time of the storytelling. However, if they are written down in their life story book the story lives on and becomes part of the person's recorded history.

Style

It is always preferable to write a life story book by hand. This is because a typewritten document gives the appearance of completeness and people are less likely to add to such a document. Also, a handwritten document appears less formal and more personal. In theory it should be easier to add to a handwritten book by jotting down a story and slotting it in. Not everyone has access to computers or feels competent using them.

Do not feel you have to have natural artistic ability to compile a life story book. You will see from the examples presented throughout this book that styles vary and this is what makes every book unique. Formatting can be kept simple or can be as extravagant as you want to make it. This should depend on the wishes and abilities of the person whose book it is.

Even if it is difficult for the person to actively illustrate their book, and you do not feel you are very artistic, there are many ways the style of the book can be enhanced. For example, from most stationers and specialist craft shops you can buy stickers and coloured shapes and templates that can be used to frame a story. Bright pens and glitter are another simple way to bring a page alive, and can be fun to create. Remember the role of pride and how good a person will feel if their own efforts are presented in their book.

Try and make use of anything around you that will help to illustrate the individual stories. For example, if writing a story about a trip to a zoo, cut out pictures of animals from magazines and use them on the relevant page. If you have a scanner there are a multitude of effects that can be achieved very easily. For example, you can scan a photograph into the computer and print a whole page of tiny prints. These can then be used to make a border to the page highlighting the main focus of the particular story.

Any keepsakes that are important to the person make interesting additions to their book, for example any tickets or programmes of events attended or postcards of places visited. Not only do they enhance the stories, they are also kept safe in the book and can be appreciated by the person at any time.

Third party input

It should never be assumed that all the stories presented have come from the person themself, as sometimes this is not the case. Words should never be put into the mouth of the person whose life story book it is. It is essential that the authorship of each story is made clear. For example, if a story being presented has been supplied by the person's mother this needs to be articulated: 'Carl's mother remembers one time when they were on a holiday in Blackpool. Carl loved watching the donkeys on the beach.'

This is preferable to suggesting in a statement that Carl loved donkeys when he was little. The story above makes it clear that it is his mother who recalls the holiday and makes the assumption that Carl enjoyed watching the donkeys. This is still valuable information and should not be viewed as inferior, because the recollections of family members and others are still essential for building up a picture of a person's history. The first person pronoun should only be used if the person themself has written the story.

Presenting photographs

Photographs really add a lot to a story. They are far easier to engage with than the written word. They allow you to view the relationships between the person and others who are, or have been, in their life. They also provide so much more information than written stories. For these reasons it is important to include as many photographs as possible in a life story book.

There are some useful tips to remember when using photographs:

- **Gain consent:** Where possible you should get consent from all the people presented on a given photograph. Sometimes this is not possible if the identity of the person is unknown or they have not had contact with the person for many years. This is not usually a problem as most people feel flattered to be included in a person's life story book.

- **Make copies:** Some photographs, especially old ones, will be very precious to the owner. Promise the owner that you will take care of the photographs, copy them and return the originals to them. This is easy to achieve either by scanning the photograph or having copies made in a photographic shop. Scanning is preferable as you can keep copies on file.

- **Label clearly:** It is important to date all photographs and write a list of all the people presented. It can be very frustrating to look at a photograph and not have any accompanying information. Try and find out as much information as possible for each photograph.

Variations on a theme

Life story books do not have to be of the type described above. Scrapbook-style life story books are the most common but life story information can be presented in a multitude of different and creative ways. This section describes some of these variations.

Posters

The easiest way to present a person's life history is to put the information on a poster. This can be achieved quickly and with maximum input from the person. All that is required are a few artefacts such as photographs and other personal effects and some glue. A poster can be put on the person's bedroom wall and shown to whoever they choose.

Having a poster may inspire the person to compile a more descriptive life story, such as a scrapbook. In this sense the poster can be viewed as either a means to a detailed life story or an end in itself.

One example of a poster-style life story is the one presented in chapter 1. A few pieces of information can reveal a lot of information about a person's identity. Another example is shown below.

Example of a poster-style life story

Computerised life stories

A life history can be compiled on a computer. If the person uses a computer regularly, such as for communication purposes, this method can be particularly appropriate. The degree of sophistication of presentation is completely at the discretion of the individual. It is essential that someone with reasonable IT skills is available to help.

Voice recognition computer software allows the person to tell their story verbally into a microphone attached to their computer. This is then converted into written text. These systems vary considerably in terms of the level of sophistication and some training is required to ensure that the computer can recognise the individual's voice.

Even on a regular PC you can compile a personal life history. It can be as simple as writing it in a Word document, adding scanned photographs and any artistic effects contained in the computer (such as Clip Art). With more advanced computer knowledge it is possible to develop a fully interactive life story, using multimedia technology. It is then possible for the person to navigate their way through their life history, interacting with any elements they wish to explore further. Sound effects and digitised recorded interviews of themself and significant others can be added. The possibilities are endless, and how far you go will depend on both the skills of the person whose life story it is and the level of support given to produce the life story on the computer.

One major thing to remember if considering a computerised life story is that computers are fallible. When producing a life story in a standard Word document it may be a good idea save it on a floppy disc or CD. It may also be prudent to print a hard copy in case the information gets lost.

Video diaries

A life history can be presented as a video diary. This is another very animated medium that does not require the viewer to be able to read. A video is easy to engage with and allows the person to document any given moment. Over time you can accumulate a whole library of videos. Again, the possibilities are endless but there are a few things to bear in mind when considering producing a life story on video:

- Video as many relatives and friends of the person as possible. It is special to hear other peoples' recollections of your life and particularly important if family members are old. A video recording of them will keep their memory alive even when they have passed on.

- Include footage of significant photographs in the video. Commentary can explain who is in the picture and where and when it was taken. In this sense the video can be seen as a recording of the life story interviews described in chapter 6.

- Always catalogue the videos and keep them in some kind of order. It is frustrating to have to view hours of footage to find a particular segment.

- Like computers, videos are also fallible. It is therefore important to produce back-ups of your material.

Bag books

Bag books are sensory enhanced 'books' developed for people with profound multiple and sensory impairments (Fuller, 2000; Lambe and Watson, 2002). They are built up on large pieces of card with objects of reference pertaining to the stories that are recognisable to the person. Each piece of card may only have one item on it but collectively they will relay a story that will be told and retold to the person several times at regular intervals. Over time it is possible to observe anticipation as the person comes to recognise the order of the story.

Bag books can convey any story from simple daily events, such as going to the shops, to more personal stories. A life story could be developed by putting something personal on each piece of card. For example, if the person likes going swimming, a piece of their towel with the smell of chlorine could be used to symbolise this activity. An enlarged photograph of a family member and objects from the family home could be stuck on a piece of card. Likewise objects from holidays could be used to symbolise places visited. For example, sand and shells can evoke memories of beaches. This would be enhanced further if the smell of the sea could be captured in the shells. Other special times such as Christmas can be represented by a shiny decoration. Christmas decorations often have an aroma that can be enhanced by spraying them with some fern fragrance.

More information on bag books can be found on the websites listed in the resources section.

Memory boxes

A memory box, like a bag book, provides a more sensory enhanced experience. Objects of importance can be kept in a special box and handled as and when desired. Memory boxes are very tactile, which makes them particularly appropriate for people with sensory impairments who rely on senses other than sight. Anything can be collected and put into the memory box as long as it has personal significance to the individual. Here are some suggestions:

- photographs of significant people in their life

- photographs of themselves when young

- wrist bands from hospital stays

- pieces of fabric from various important places (such as their parents' home)

- souvenirs from trips and holidays

- tickets from important events attended

- birth certificate

- items belonging to loved ones (such as jewellery or clothing)

- material sprayed with familiar perfume or aromatherapy oils

- tapes of favourite music

The list is endless and will depend solely on the person. Items can be added or removed as desired with ease. This format also requires the least intervention from the helper. Nothing needs to be mounted, just placed in a box, so the person has more control over what goes into the box.

All the above formats can be tried exclusively or combined with other formats to produce a multimedia life story. The choice is vast and depends ultimately on the wishes and needs of the individual. There is no harm trying one format then moving to another type. Life stories are evolving all the time and this should be reflected in the life story books created.

Summary

This chapter has presented advice and suggestions for compiling a life story once all the relevant information has been gathered. The books should never become prescriptive, so each new project needs to be approached with an open mind in order to produce an idiosyncratic life story book unique to the individual.

Another aim of this chapter has been to demonstrate the many different ways life story information can be presented. It does not have to be in the shape of a book. Posters, video diaries, computer-generated versions, bag books and memory books are just some of the variations you can try. If one method is not successful there are always alternatives to try.

Chapter 8

Just the beginning

Once the life history information has been collected and presented in the preferred format the worst thing that can happen is that it is put on a shelf to gather dust. Life story books are evolving resources and should be added to as and when something significant happens. While the person is still alive their life story book is never complete.

This chapter summarises the main messages presented in the book, starting by reiterating the importance of having a life story, then dispelling some of the myths about life story books that may prevent you from starting a project. The book ends by encouraging you to reflect on what has been presented and hopefully inspiring you to proceed with a life story project of your own.

The value of life story books

By now the benefits of owning a life story book should be clear. They are a resource that highlights a person's identity, which is fundamental to developing a sense of self. Having a clearly defined identity is also essential for forming and maintaining relationships. We relate to other people by having a sense of who they are, and this is achieved by sharing stories and experiences of your past.

How care staff use life story books

An earlier study (Hewitt, 1998; 2000) showed how staff in a residential setting used the life story books of six clients in their care. Once the life story books had been compiled and placed in the care setting, data was collected to see how the books were received and used. Three main sources of data were used:

- **Comments page:** At the back of each life story book a comments page was placed. Anyone reading the book was asked to write their initial thoughts, reactions and feelings after reading the book for the first time.

- **Staff meetings:** Meetings were recorded where the life story books were discussed as part of the agenda. This was a good opportunity for staff to share their views on the books they had read.

- **Additions to the books:** Once the books had been compiled and given to the individuals in the setting, it was the responsibility of the carers to make any necessary additions as and when anything notable happened. The books were revisited a year after initial compilation and any additions were noted.

On analysing these comments and additions to the original life story books the following three uses were highlighted. Life story books were viewed as a useful resource for:

- **Getting to know the person:** The books were seen as a better introduction to the person than their care plan which tends to be very function-orientated. People felt that the life story books were a way of getting to know the person quicker because they had access to information regarding their relationships and past experiences. This obviously has implications for new staff in terms of getting to know the people they are working with. The books were seen as valuable for established members of staff and new starters alike. Every person who read the books, regardless of how long they had known the person, learnt something new. Some comments are presented below.

> 'I think the most important aspect of the life stories is that they portray a history of an individual that would otherwise be passed by; and it is the humanness, the dignity and respect that everybody deserves and has a right to expect. Having known Jane for only a short time it has given me a closer insight into Jane as a person in her own right.'
>
> New member of staff

Clearly this new member of staff found the life story book helpful for getting to know Jane. He displays sensitivity to her identity as an individual rather than as just a client.

'Easy to read and I know a lot more about Sharon now. A useful book for all new carers in any setting. I wish it was there to read a few years ago.'

Established member of staff

This established member of staff talks about getting to know the clients as an ongoing process. Despite having worked in the setting for over five years she suggests the books are useful for discovering more about the person's history.

- **Defining the person:** The books were also used as a way of defining the person in wider terms than as just a client in the present. Reading the stories and seeing photographs of the person with the important people in their life helps carers to view the person as having several identities and not just as a recipient of care. They can be seen as sons, daughters, sisters, brothers, friends and colleagues to the various people who have played a part in their lives, both past and present. The following comments highlight this.

'It was nice to see photos of Jackie as a baby and what a nice relationship she has with her family.'

Established member of staff

This staff member, despite having worked in this setting for over eight years, appears to be acknowledging the relationships Jackie has with her family for the first time. Jackie's identity as a member of a family is being highlighted.

'This book really shows the length of Sharon and Jackie's relationship and why they are together now.'

Residential manager

Here the manager is talking about Jackie and Sharon as being friends rather than two clients who happen to live in the same setting.

- **Displaying personality:** Life story books were also used as a means of displaying the individual's personality. Direct comparisons were made between the care plans and life story books, with carers suggesting that life story books display the personality of the person as opposed to just presenting their needs and schedule of care. Here is a typical comment that reflects this.

'People can get a real picture of how somebody is and what their personality is, just like the information we'd know about each other, rather than this person has epilepsy or something like that.'

Established member of staff during a staff meeting

Here, this established member of staff suggests that the life story books tell you more about someone's personality than the information in their care plans.

Although the uses highlighted are essential for the creation and maintenance of the identity of the person with learning disabilities, they are mainly focused on the carer's use of the books. More importantly, life story books enable the person themself to view their life as an unfolding narrative and make sense of the relationships and events they have engaged in. They also allow the person to feel a sense of pride at having a book in which they are the central focus. The combinations of uses described throughout this book all benefit the person because, by encouraging others to define the person in wider terms than 'client' and allowing them to see their personality, they are more likely to be treated as a unique individual. This is the central tenet of person-centred planning, which puts the person at the heart of their own care. A life story book is a way of introducing the person before their needs and schedule of care.

Dispelling the myths

Most people will think that a life story book is a huge task to undertake. The thought of compiling someone's life history can appear daunting and will put most people off right at the start. However, it should be clear by now that starting a life story project can be very straightforward and a book can actually be up and running in a short time. You just need the courage and motivation to get started. Chapter 5 provides advice and tips for planning the project, while chapter 6 details the skills needed for collecting the information.

A perceived hurdle that may put people off is the fact that some people with learning disabilities do not have any living relatives and few contacts from their distant past. Rather than seeing this as a hurdle, view it as a starting point to explore the person's history. There will be medical records and a care history of the person that will provide details of the places they have lived previously. A few telephone calls can yield many contacts who can help to fill in the gaps. Remember that a life history does not have to begin with the birth of the person. It can begin at any point in the person's life and, as long as it is added to the life story, will evolve in time.

Another myth associated with life story books is that you need to be extremely artistic to create an interesting biography. Again, it should be apparent by now how easy it is to compile a lively colourful book, or other form of life story, by simply adding photographs and other personal effects. Chapter 7 outlines the different ways of presenting a life story and advice on styles and formatting.

So there really should be no reason to reject the notion of compiling a life story book unless, of course, the person does not want to produce one. A life story project should only be initiated when it is the right time for the person. Wherever possible they need to take the lead. The books should not become prescriptive documents like care plans because that would defeat the very object of them which is to highlight the individuality of the person. This is hard to achieve if everyone has a set format. It is a myth that you need to know the formula for producing life story books. You really have free reign to produce a book that reflects the uniqueness of the individual.

Over to you

Now you have read through this guide, you should be equipped with the knowledge and skills to make a start. You may already have people in mind to whom you would like to introduce the notion of a life story book. Read the exercise below to help you reflect on how you can proceed with a life story project.

Exercise 4 - how to proceed with a life story project

Think about someone who you feel would benefit from having a life story book. Ask yourself the following questions:

- Why would they benefit from having a life story book?

- Are they able to understand the concept of life story books?

- If not, how are you going to introduce the idea?

- How can you engage the person to participate as much as possible?

- Who would you contact to contribute to the book?

Once you have answered these questions you are half way to starting a life story project. Now all you need to do is to make it happen.

Summary

The following sentences sum up the main messages of this book:

● Look beyond the 'client' identity, because we all have a unique life history.

● A life story book is never complete. It is evolving and needs to be added to.

● Always keep the person at the centre of their life story project.

● Enjoy the process.

References

Atkinson, D. (1997) *An Autobiographical Approach to Learning Disability Research.* Open University Press: Milton Keynes

Atkinson, D., McCarthy, M., Walmsley, J., Cooper, M., Rolph, S., Aspis, S., Barette, P., Coventry, M. and Ferris, G. (eds) (2000) *Good Times, Bad Times: Women with Learning Difficulties Telling their Stories.* BILD: Kidderminster

Bogdan, R. and Taylor, S. J. (1989) Relationships with severely disabled people: the social construction of humanness. *Social Problems* 36, 135–148

Bogdan, R. and Taylor, S. J. (1994) *The Social Meaning of Mental Retardation – Two Life Stories.* New York: Teachers College Press

Brigham, L., Atkinson, D., Jackson, M., Rolph, S. and Walmsley, J. (2000) *Crossing Boundaries: Change and Continuity in the History of Learning Disability.* BILD: Kidderminster

Department of Health (2001) *Valuing people: a new strategy for learning disability for the 21st century.* London: HMSO

Edgerton, R. B. (1967) *The Cloak of Competence.* Berkeley: University of California Press

Fray, M.T. (2000) *Caring for Kathleen: A Sister's Story about Down's Syndrome and Dementia.* BILD: Kidderminster

Goffman, E. (1963) *Stigma.* Englewood Cliffs, NJ: Prentice-Hall

Hewitt, H. (1997) *Identities in Transition: Formulating Care for People with Profound Learning Disabilities.* Unpublished Ph.D. thesis (Loughborough University)

Hewitt, H. (1998) Life story books for people with learning disabilities. *Nursing Times* 94(33) 61–63

Hewitt, H. (2000) A life story approach for people with profound learning disabilities. *British Journal of Nursing* 9(2) 90–95

Hewitt, H. (2003) Tell it like it is: life story books for people with learning disabilities. *Learning Disability Practice* 6(8) 18–22

Laverty, H. and Reet, M. (2001) *Planning Care for Children in Respite Settings: 'Hello this is me'.* Jessica Kingsley: London

Linde, C. (1993) *Life Stories: The Creation of Coherence.* Oxford: Oxford University Press

O'Brien, J. and Tyne, A. (1981) *The Principle of Normalisation: A Foundation for Effective Services.* London: The Campaign for Mentally Handicapped People

Pietrukowicz, M. E. and Johnson, M. M. S.
(1991) Using life histories to individualize
nursing home staff attitudes toward residents.
The Gerontologist 31, 102–106

Ryan, T. and Walker, R. (1985) *Making Life
Story Books* (1st edn). London: BAAF

Ryan, T. and Walker, R. (eds) (1993)
Life Story Work. London: BAAF

Szivos, S. E. and Griffiths, E. (1990)
Group processes involved in coming to
terms with a mentally retarded identity.
Mental Retardation 28, 333–341

Szivos, S. E. and Griffiths, E. (1990)
Consciousness raising and social identity
theory: a challenge to normalisation.
Clinical Psychology Forum 28, 11–15

Taylor, T. (2003) *Insistent Voices:
Stories on Claiming Identity.* Kingston
Advocacy Group: Kingston upon Thames

Wolfensberger, W. (1972) *The Principles of
Normalization in Human Services.* Toronto:
National Institute of Mental Retardation

Wolfensberger, W. (1983)
Social role valorisation: a proposed new name for
normalization. *Mental Retardation* 21, 234–239